_____ MY LITTLE BOOK ABOUT _____

THE MIRACLE OF EASTER

NEW SEASONS

PUBLISHING

© 1993 Publications International, Ltd.
ISBN 0-7853-0089-9
Adapted by Etta G. Wilson
Illustrations by Thomas Gianni
Made in the U.S.A.

The people who had known Jesus were very sad when he died. A man named Joseph from Arimathea went to the Roman governor Pilate. He asked Pilate if he could bury Jesus' body, and Pilate agreed.

Joseph took the body, wrapped it in a clean sheet, and prepared it for burial. With the help of some friends, Joseph laid Jesus' body in a new tomb that had been carved out of solid rock. Then they rolled a large stone across the opening of the tomb.

The next day, the government leaders remembered what Jesus had said: "After three days I will rise again."

They went to Pilate and got permission to have guards watch the tomb.

That Sunday, something very strange happened at the tomb. An earthquake shook the earth, and an angel appeared. He rolled away the stone that closed the tomb and sat on it. Then Jesus came out of his tomb. The guards were so afraid. They trembled and fell down, as though they were dead.

Later, Mary Magdalene, a friend of Jesus, went to the tomb with some other women. When they arrived, they were surprised to find that the tomb was empty.

Inside the tomb, they saw an angel. The angel said, "Don't be afraid. Jesus is not here. He has risen just as he said he would. See for yourselves! Quickly now, go tell his followers that Jesus is alive again! You will see him in Galilee."

After leaving the tomb, Mary Magdalene and the other women ran to find the disciples. They told them the exciting news about the empty tomb.

Most of the disciples thought the women were wrong, but Peter and John ran to the tomb. John got there first. He saw the strips of cloth lying on the floor, but he didn't go in.

When Peter got there, he went straight into the tomb. He saw the linen cloths and the cloth that had been around Jesus' head. Then John went in. Both of them saw that Jesus' body was not there. The tomb was empty!

Quickly, they returned to tell the other disciples.

That same day, two of Jesus' disciples were going to a village outside Jerusalem. They were talking about everything that had happened. As they talked, another man came along and walked with them. It was Jesus, but the men didn't recognize him.

"What are you talking about?" Jesus asked.

The two disciples stopped and looked at him. One of them said, "You must be the only man in the city who doesn't know what has happened."

"What do you mean?" Jesus asked.

Then both of them explained about what had happened to Jesus.

Then Jesus asked the two disciples, "Why can't you understand? How can you be so slow to believe what the prophets said?"

Jesus began to explain everything that had been written about him by the prophets. The prophets were people who had predicted Jesus' coming long ago. As Jesus talked they came into the village. The two disciples asked Jesus to spend the night with them.

While they were at the table eating together, Jesus took a loaf of bread, blessed it, and gave it to the disciples. At that moment they knew he was Jesus. Then he disappeared from the room. The disciples were amazed! They went straight back to Jerusalem to tell the other disciples that they had seen Jesus.

That same night, most of the disciples were together in Jerusalem. They were in a house with the doors locked. Suddenly, Jesus was standing there with them. He showed them the wounds in his wrists and his side, so they knew he was really Jesus. They were so happy. Thomas, one of the disciples, was not with them that night. When the others told him what had happened, he did not believe them.

A week later all the disciples were together again. And again the doors were locked. Once more, Jesus came to them and greeted them. He called Thomas over and said, "Touch the wounds in my wrists and my side. Stop doubting and believe!"

Thomas answered, "My Lord, I believe in you."

Jesus told the disciples to go to a hill they knew in Galilee and he would meet them there. They left their place in Jerusalem and went out to the hillside.

There they saw Jesus coming. The disciples fell down and worshiped him.

Jesus came closer and began to speak to them. "God has given me power over everything. Now I ask you to go to all people everywhere and make them my disciples. Baptize them and teach them to obey what I have taught you. And don't forget, I will be with you forever."

Then Jesus raised his hands and blessed them. As he was blessing them, he was taken up into heaven.

They went back to Jerusalem and straight into the Temple. There they gave thanks to God for the wonderful things that had happened.